Native Orchids
of the Eastern
Caribbean

●

JULIAN KENNY

MACMILLAN
CARIBBEAN

First published 1988 by
MACMILLAN EDUCATION LTD
London and Oxford
Companies and representatives throughout the world

www.macmillan-caribbean.com

ISBN 0–333–47330–2

15	14	13	12	11	10	9	8	7	6
10	09	08	07	06	05	04	03	02	01

This book is printed on paper suitable for recycling and
made from fully managed and sustained forest sources.

Printed in Hong Kong

A catalogue record for this book is available from the
British Library.

Contents

For Joan

Acknowledgements

The author wishes to thank Drs Dennis Adams and Julien Duncan for their encouragement in writing this guide and Dr Phillip Cribb of Kew for confirming several new records from Trinidad. Thanks are also due to P. Badal, I. Singh and R. Mahabir for assistance in the field and to Y. Comeau for help in the National Herbarium. Special thanks are due to Professor G. M. Sammy who loaned rare local species from his collection for photography and to Mr R. F. Barnes for leading the author to the very rare *Habenaria pauciflora* in the field. The author wishes to thank also Jo and John Rickards of St Lucia who took time to introduce him to the native orchids of that country.

The author wishes also to thank two of his students, Caroline Chaboo and Graham White for help in the field and wishes that they will ultimately be able to see the rest of the native orchids of Trinidad. Finally the author is particularly indebted to Gabriella Gray who was responsible for preparation of the final draft and the manuscript and to Pauline Tait and Bill Lennox who introduced him to an entirely new experience.

All the photographs in the book, including the cover photographs, were taken by the author.

Cover   Coryanthes macrantha
Coryanthes macrantha, known in Trinidad as the Monkey Throat orchid is a common species in secondary forests. It produces a single flower at a time which is almost always fertilised. The flower produces a chemical attractant which will draw in several euglossine bees from the surrounding forest. The form of the flower is such that bees fall into the bowl of the lip and can only leave by passing through a small apperture between the edge of the lip and the column. As it

does this the large pollinia are glued to the thorax of the bee. On visiting another flower the pollinia attach to the stigmatic surface.

Back Cover

Orchids are found in a wide range of habitats. Tropical savannahs are nutrient poor from leaching of soils. Many orchids live in such habitats. The Aripo Savannahs in Eastern Trinidad are the home of many ground orchids such as *Pogonia rosea* seen growing in a small island of vegetation.

Preface

This book deals with a little over a hundred of the native orchids of the Lesser Antilles. The orchid family is an extremely diverse group of plants and the only definitive means of species identification is a thorough examination of the flower. As with most orchids, there is a distinct flowering season and with most of the Antillian species, the season is short and plants flower generally only once. It is therefore unlikely that the layperson would be able readily to determine a species in the field. The orchid flora of the region consists of elements which are widely distributed throughout northern South America, Central America, the south-east United States and the Greater Antilles but there are a number of endemic species. The total flora amounts to about 200 species in about 80 genera. Orchids all show varying degrees of habitat preference and while it would be desirable to organise this book in terms of various habitats, this approach would make it extremely difficult for the layreader. A compromise is made and a more formal systematic treatment is employed. A full tabulation of the orchid flora of the region is given at the end of the book, but no attempt is made to deal with this on the basis of individual islands. Instead, a full listing is given for Trinidad and one for the rest of the Eastern Caribbean. In some instances, for example *Spiranthes,* a conservative nomenclature is employed although the genus has been split.

In most of the islands, it is inevitable that one can find at least one person who is not only interested in native orchids but one who maintains living collections. One of the quickest ways of learning the orchid flora is to establish contact with such people.

The twin Pitons above the village of Souffriere in St Lucia are the home of many orchids.

Introduction

The family Orchidaceae is probably one of the largest families of plants. It is only rivalled in size by the grasses and the composites. No one knows how many species there are but estimates range from 20,000 to 35,000 species.

Orchids are widely distributed throughout the world being absent only from Antartica. In temperate climates they are all terrestrial but in the tropics and sub-tropics they are largely epiphytic in habitat. Two areas of the world with the largest orchid floras are South East Asia and North West South America. Possibly the area with the largest orchid flora is the foothills of the Andes in Ecuador.

Orchids live in a wide range of habitats. Many are terrestrial but by and large, most are epiphytic. Some species may be both terrestrial and epiphytic and some may be rock-dwelling or lithophytic. Many species may be found in semi-aquatic conditions such as bogs or herbaceous swamps but there are no truly aquatic species. One Australian species is sub-terranean and a few are saprophytic. Many species show a remarkable tolerance to extremes of environment and many epiphytic species can withstand prolonged dehydration, while a few can be found living in the splash zone on the sea coast.

Orchids generally may be regarded as small plants and they range in size from a few millimetres in height to vines such as *Vanilla* which measure in excess of 30 m. Most however fall within the range of 10 to 50 cm. Two general growth patterns may be seen in orchids (Figure 1). In some, growth may be sympodial, where at the end of a season, growth stops and a new stem appears at the start of the next growing season. In cases such as this, the base of the old stem may be variously enlarged to form a structure called a pseudobulb which is an organ for storage of both water and nutrients. Some orchids

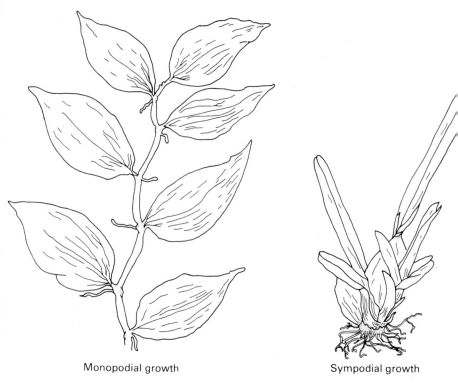

Monopodial growth   Sympodial growth

Figure 1

grow continuously and this form of growth is referred to as monopodial growth. The common *Cattleya* orchid, much fancied by horticulturists, shows typical sympodial growth. The *Vanilla* orchid is an example of a species showing monopodial growth.

Leaves of orchids are extremely variable. In many species the stem may produce a single leaf but more commonly leaves are multiple and alternate. Leaves are parallel-veined and vary in texture from being papery to leathery. In some species the leaves may be very much reduced or even absent, for example, *Habenaria*. Some epiphytic species, for example, *Campylocentrum* are entirely leafless and the roots are modified for photosynthesis. A saprophytic species, *Wullschlaegelia,* is totally without leaves and is only seen when the flower stalk emerges from decaying litter material on the forest floor.

2

In epiphytic orchids the roots are generally comparatively few in number and fleshy. A special feature of the orchid root is the external layer called velamen which is a multi-layered structure consisting of sponge-like cells which serve both for adhesion and water storage. In terrestrial orchids the roots tend to be fewer, lacking a velamen layer and are frequently enlarged to form tuberoids which are storage organs. Indeed in many of the species of terrestrial orchids, superficial vegetative growth dies back at the end of each growing season and the tuberoids serve to carry over the plant to the following growing season.

While there is no doubt that there is considerable diversity of form of vegetative growth, it is the floral form which shows the most striking diversity and which attracts the interest of horticulturists and naturalists. Orchids are thought to be of comparatively recent origin and probably arose in South East Asia from the common line of plants which gave rise to the Irises and Lilies. The trimerous symmetry of the flower is shared by these groups but in the orchids there are several striking features. In this family, as in the others, there are three sepals and three petals. One of the three petals (Figure 2) is modified to form a structure called the lip or labellum and this serves as a platform on which pollinators may alight prior to pollination. This dissimilar third petal gives a bilateral symmetry to the orchid flower. Flowers of this kind are said to be zygomorphic. Although in some species the lip varies slightly in form and colour from the other petals and sepals,

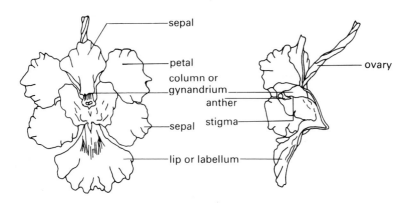

Figure 2

generally the lip is strikingly coloured or highly modified morphologically.

The reproductive parts of the flower are fused to form an entirely new structure called the column or a gynandrium and it is this particular feature which separates off the orchids from the rest of the monocotyledonous plants (Figure 2). In primitive orchids there are two fertile stamens. In most orchids however, one stamen is fertile and bears the anther terminally. The stigmata may be somewhat variable and in the more highly evolved orchids the three stigmatic surfaces fuse into a single one which faces the lip. In some, a part of the stigma called a rostellum projects outward and serves to glue the pollen masses to the visiting pollinator. In others a sticky pad called the viscidium which is derived from the rostellum may be detached with the pollen grains as a unit. The anther usually contains two to eight pollen masses which range in texture from being soft and waxy to hard. The pollen masses are an important characteristic used in the classification of orchids.

In orchids the ovary is inferior and in most, on development of the flower, the ovary undergoes a 180° twisting which brings the lip into a ventral position. This feature is referred to as resupination. Once pollinated the perianth usually wilts rapidly and growth of the ovary commences. In most orchids the column becomes swollen after pollination. In many species this is a slow process which may take months leading to the production of a dehiscent pod which on splitting releases vast quantities of microscopic seeds. Orchid seeds are usually elongate, dust-like and lack an endosperm or any other food storage structure. On germinating, an orchid seed commences to swell within the seed coat and forms a protocorm with a vegetative apex.

The protocorm usually flattens and produces leaflets. Roots emerge subsequent to this and germination and growth are usually extremely slow processes. It is not unusual for larger species to take several years of growth before their first flowering. In order for an orchid to germinate it is necessary for a special fungus to infect the seed. It is this fungus which forms a permanent association with the roots and enables orchids to grow in nutrient-deficient environments.

In a group as complex and as numerous as this family, it is inevitable that there will be differences of opinions on classification at the level of sub-family. One classification of

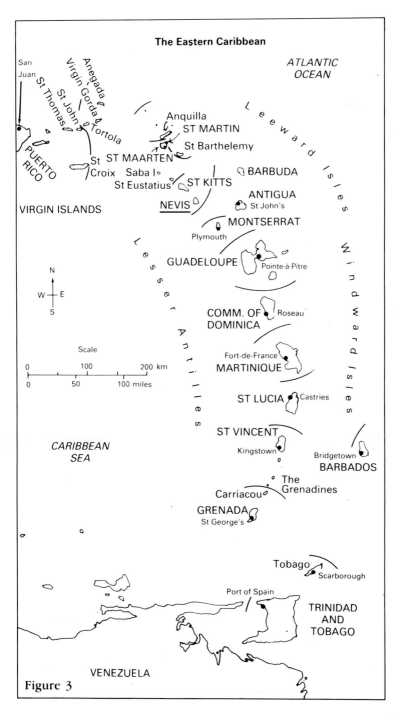

The Eastern Caribbean

Figure 3

the family which appears to have wide acceptance recognises five sub-families which are:

Apostasioideae, Cypripedioideae, Orchidoideae, Neottioideae and Epidendroideae.

Of these five families only the last four are found in the Eastern Caribbean.

The Eastern Caribbean consists of a chain of islands extending from the Paria peninsula of Venezuela northward to Puerto Rico (Figure 3). The islands are generally small with Trinidad being the largest with a land area of about 1,680 sq. miles. The chain of islands consists of an eastern outer arc of limestone islands such as Barbados, the eastern half of Guadaloupe, Antigua and Barbuda, and a western inner arc of volcanic origin of significantly higher elevations. The islands have been colonised for a period of almost 500 years and this has had a pronounced effect on general vegetation. In some islands, for example, Barbados, there is virtually no natural vegetation remaining. In other islands such as Martinique, Guadaloupe, St Lucia, St Vincent and Grenada, there remains some natural vegetation especially at higher elevations. Only two of these islands have any extensive stands of primary forest; these are Dominica to the north and Trinidad to the south.

In all the islands there is still to be seen considerable variation in forest type, ranging from mangroves along the sea coast to thorny scrub grasslands and herbaceous swamps. None of these commonly support significant orchid floras and it is only when one moves into the montane formations that significant numbers of orchids may be found.

With 500 years of colonisation and extreme change to vegetation, it is inevitable that the native orchid floras must necessarily be different. Not only have we had problems of denudation of forest, there is no doubt that there has also been considerable movement of plant material of different kinds for horticultural purposes. Indeed today the most commonly seen orchids in the Eastern Caribbean are horticultural varieties of exotic species brought from the Far East and from northern South America. On the other hand, human activity has very clearly influenced the abundance of many species. A visit to a cocoa plantation in the Eastern Caribbean will demonstrate

The largest numbers of orchids are to be found in montane forests in islands such as Trinidad, St Lucia and Dominica.

the effects of agriculture on orchid abundance. For unknown reasons, cocoa is favoured by orchids, particularly of the genera *Maxillaria* and *Pleurothallis*.

No one really knows how many native orchids may be found in the Eastern Caribbean. Within the Windward and Leeward Islands there have been recorded 141 species in 44 genera, while in Trinidad almost 200 species in about 80 genera have been recorded. In the case of Trinidad, new records are being made frequently, with well over a dozen having been added to Schultes' list. Most of the native orchids flower seasonally and in many cases the flowers are short-lived and minute. However, there are many showy orchids, particularly of the genus *Oncidium,* which can stand beside the most striking of horticultural varieties. There are however none of any commercial importance in the horticultural trade, although some are sought after by collectors. In terms of numbers of species the genus *Epidendrum* is clearly the most important. Other important genera are *Maxillaria, Pleurothallis, Habenaria* and *Spiranthes*. There is clearly a typical flora for the Lesser Antilles which contains a number of endemic species and a Trinidad flora which is typically South American.

There is an extensive literature on the family Orchidaceae but the serious naturalist need only refer to the Garay and Sweet (1974), Schultes (1967) and Dunsterville and Garay (1979). Garay and Sweet cover the orchids of the Windward and Leeward Islands while Schultes deals with Trinidad and Tobago. Both these publications give comprehensive botanical descriptions. Dunsterville and Garay give excellent line drawings of the orchids of Venezuela, reprinted from the earlier six volume work.

Dunsterville, G. C. K. and Garay, L. A. (1979). *Orchids of Venezuela. An illustrated field guide.* Harvard University.

Howard, R. A. (1974). *Flora of the Lesser Antilles.* [Section: Orchidaceae. Garay, L. A. and Sweet, H. R.] Harvard University.

Schultes, R. F. (1967). *Flora of Trinidad and Tobago.* [Section: Orchidaceae.] Government Printery, Trinidad and Tobago. Vol. 3, No. 1

Sub-family:

CYPRIPEDIOIDEAE

This sub-family which includes a number of showy ground-dwelling orchids in the Northern Hemisphere, is represented by only one species in the Lesser Antilles and this, only in Trinidad. The sub-family is characterised by having two fertile stamens and the dorsal sepal is enlarged and showy, while the lip forms a deep pocket. *Selenepedium palmifolium* has no common name in Trinidad and may be considered rare. Unlike most of the Lady Slipper orchids, this species may attain considerable height. It is not uncommon to find plants in excess of 2 m tall and occasionally 3 m tall. The vegetative form of the species is rather grass-like and when not in flower, it may easily be missed. The species appears to favour poor acidic soils and intermediate shade. It has an extensive flowering period lasting several months but only one flower is produced at a time.

Sub-family:

ORCHIDOIDEAE

This sub-family includes a large number of genera, all of which are terrestrial. Unlike the Lady Slippers, there is only one fertile stamen and there may be two or three confluent stigmata; the third one is frequently abortive and no rostellum is present. The family is well represented in the Northern Hemisphere in a wide range of habitats. Only one genus is present in the Lesser Antilles, *Habenaria*.

The genus *Habenaria* includes mostly small terrestrial or semi-aquatic plants which possess fleshy tuberoids. Stems are invariably erect and leaves frequently much reduced. The lip has characteristically at its base an elongate downward projecting structure called a spur which produces nectar. The flowers are usually green and rarely showy. Some are extremely common such as *Habenaria mesodactyla* while others are only known from two or three records, for example *Habenaria pauciflora*. While common and widely distributed each species has quite narrow habitat preference. Ten species have been recorded from the Lesser Antilles.

Sub-family:

NEOTTIOIDEAE

This large sub-family differs from the Orchidoideae largely in the form of the pollinia and in the development of the rostellum. The pollen grains form loosely adhering, but distinct firm masses. In the Lesser Antilles the family is represented by an extremely large and divergent number of mainly terrestrial species. Some are large and showy, while others may be small and insignificant. The principal genera represented include *Spiranthes, Vanilla, Pogonia, Cranichis* and *Erythrodes* but there are a total of 12 genera in the region.

The genus *Pogonia* is represented by three species found in Trinidad. None of these occur in the rest of the Lesser Antilles. *Pogonia rosea* is one of the most striking of the ground orchids found in savannah conditions. Mature plants are up to about half metre tall and have a characteristic bluish tinge to the leaves. This species flowers in the early part of the rainy season and dies back towards the end of the rainy season. The flowers which are borne in the axils of the leaves number two or occasionally three and they are large and showy. The species is quite common but confined to the special conditions of the savannah. *Pogonia tenuis* is a less visible but common species found in the open savannah. Plants measure up to about 10 cm. This latter species has a very short-lived flowering in the early part of the rainy season, dying back almost immediately. A third species, *Pogonia grandiflora* may be regarded as rare in Trinidad.

Vanilla is a common genus in the Lesser Antilles and it is found in northern South America and Central America. *Vanilla* forms large vines which ascend to the canopy of the forest. Most of the *Vanillas* have large, showy but short-lived flowers. The most common are *Vanilla mexicana*, which has broad papery leaves, and *Vanilla phaeantha*, which has narrow thickened leathery leaves. *Vanilla planifolia* has been recorded from most of the Lesser Antilles but not from Trinidad.

Cranichis is a tiny terrestrial orchid usually found in very moist places and sometimes associated with streams. In height it measures up to about 6 cm and its inflorescence bears a few

11

minute, white flowers with green marks. This species has been recorded from most of the islands of the Lesser Antilles but is unlikely to be recognised as an orchid unless it is in flower.

The genus *Spiranthes* includes a large number of terrestrial orchids. The genus has been divided by some authorities to include *Sarcoglottis, Stenorhynchos* and *Spiranthes.* The most common species is *Spiranthes acaulis.* This species usually has striking foliage which may be variegated, green and white or purple and green. On flowering, the leaves all die back and the inflorescence grows to a height of about 50 cm. The flowers are green, densely packed and are in a spiral. *Spiranthes acaulis* is common throughout Trinidad and has been recorded also from Grenada. Another common species is *Spiranthes cranichoides* which has been collected in wet localities in most islands of the Lesser Antilles. Perhaps the species with the widest distribution is *Spiranthes lanceolata* which has been recorded from most of the islands including even the very dry ones such as Antigua and Barbados. This species is a moderately tall species, growing up to about 15 cm and its inflorescence grows up to about 50 cm. It is a common roadside plant found frequently growing under extremely harsh conditions. The species flowers in March and the form of the flower is typical of the genus. The flowers, which are peach coloured, are arranged spirally at the end of the inflorescence. *Spiranthes* normally have fleshy tuberoids and occasionally may be found growing epiphytically. *Spiranthes costaricencis* is a common epiphyte of cocoa. Perhaps the most unusual *Spiranthes* is *Spiranthes simplex.* This species which is minute has been found only in the Aripo Savannahs in Trinidad. The leaves are very much reduced and the inflorescence bears one or occcasionally two flowers. The entire growing season lasts only about six weeks after which the plant dies back. Two tuberoids are produced and these carry the plant over from one season to the other.

Erythrodes is represented by five species in the Lesser Antilles. The species are all terrestrial and although moderately large, are easily missed in the field. They are typically found in moist places and may be found growing on rocks in river gorges. They frequently form extensive pure stands which may contain hundreds of plants. The flowers are numerous but insignificant. Both *Erythrodes plantaginea* and *Erythrodes hirtella* are common in the Lesser Antilles.

Sub-family:

EPIDENDROIDEAE

This sub-family is the largest found in the region and is closely related to the sub-family Neottioideae. The main difference is that Epidendroideae are mainly epiphytic. In contrast to the Neottioideae, members of the sub-family Epidendroideae have a long and frequently highly modified column. Both sub-families have a single fertile stamen bearing a single anther but in the former, the anther is erect while in the latter it is closely aligned to the column. The sub-family Epidendroideae is represented by about 60 different genera.

Certainly the most common genus of the sub-family is the genus *Epidendrum*. It is represented in the region by about 30 different species, many of which are large and showy and very much sought after by collectors. Plants are usually epiphytic and without a pseudobulb and the vegetative growth may be extremely variable. Some may have one or two leaves, while others have many leaves arranged alternately along the swollen stems. The inflorescence in this genus is always terminal and the lip is usually divided into three lobes. Flowers vary from few to many and some species have an extended flowering season. Some are extremely showy.

Another genus well represented in the Eastern Caribbean is *Pleurothallis.* This genus consists of mainly small densely clumped plants with fleshy leaves frequently growing in mats at different levels of the forest canopy. Some are minute with leaves measuring less than 1 cm and flowers less than 5 mm. The stems are short and the single leaves are borne on a long petiole. Flowers are usually single and frequently of bizarre form with fusion of different parts of the perianth.

The genus *Oncidium,* while not represented by a very large number of species, is certainly one of the more showy genera and also very much sought after by collectors. As a rule the species are large with a single leaf and flattened pseudobulb. The inflorescence is always lateral from the base of the pseudobulb and is many-flowered. The flowers are usually not fragrant but one species is particularly so.

A fourth genus *Maxillaria* is also a prominent genus in the region, particularly in Trinidad. The genus is a prominent element in northern South America. The plants are usually epiphytic with flattened ovoid pseudobulbs borne on elongate stems. Some however form clumps. The inflorescence is lateral from the base of the pseudobulb and may be single to many-flowered. The flowers are frequently showy but short-lived.

The above four genera account for about half of members of the sub-family in the region but other genera are worthy of note. *Schomburgkia* is commonly seen in the region but in most instances the plants are either in cultivation or escaped from cultivation. They are typically sun-dwelling species with much enlargened pseudobulbs and elongate inflorescences with showy flowers. Related to *Schomburgkia* is the genus *Cattleya* and one species has been recorded from Trinidad. Unfortunately this particular species is mostly cleistogamous. The genus *Caularthron* is represented in Trinidad by two species, one of which is extremely common, particularly along the sea coast where occasionally it may be seen growing in the splash zone. It may be either epiphytic or lithophytic. On the north-east coast of Trinidad it may be found growing in large mats on rock just above high water. It is of particular interest because it forms a relationship with a particular species of ant which lives within the base of the pseudobulb. The ant presumably provides protection to the plant.

Perhaps the most interesting orchids are those included in the genera *Catasetum, Coryanthes, Stanhopea,* and *Gongora.* Although represented by comparatively few species, all rely on euglossine bees for pollination. The genera are mainly few to single-flowered and in *Catasetum* the flowers may be dimorphic or occasionally trimorphic. *Coryanthes* produces but a single flower and this is pollinated only by *Eulaema.* The pollination of this flower was originally described by Darwin. This group of genera is not found in the Leeward and Windward Islands. There are many other genera of orchids and some of the more showy ones much sought after by collectors include *Aspasia, Bifrenaria, Brassia, Cyrtopodium,* and *Paphinia.*

The Species

CYPRIPEDIOIDEAE

Selenepedium palmifolium

This Lady Slipper orchid is the only species found in the Lesser Antilles and is confined to Trinidad. Unlike most of the Lady Slippers, this species attains considerable height, sometimes in excess of 3 m. It is a free flowering species. Vegetative growth is grass-like and hairy.

Selenepedium palmifolium

ORCHIDOIDEAE

Habenaria monorrhiza

This species is one of the larger Habenarias and is widely distributed throughout the Antilles. It is a common inhabitant of cleared lands and road cuttings. Leaves are larger than in most Habenarias and characteristically red-spotted. In Trinidad the species flowers in March. Height to about 1 m.

Habenaria monorrhiza

Habenaria leprieurii

Habenaria leprieurii

There are two species of *Habenaria* found in the Aripo
Savannahs. One of these, *Habenaria leprieurii* is not
uncommon and occurs in two forms. The more common form
has an inflorescence with the flowers bunched at the end of
it. The flowers are similar in general appearance to the more
common *Habenaria mesodactyla*. Plants have few leaves and
in most instances, these are reduced to narrow sheaths. Height
to about 40 cm.

Habenaria leprieurii var. *heptadactyla*

Habenaria mesodactyla

Habenaria leprieurii var. heptadactyla

This is the less common form of *Habenaria leprieurii* and the flowers are brilliant yellow and bunched. It is not as common as the former. Height to about 50 cm.

Habenaria mesodactyla

Habenaria mesodactyla is extremely common and numerous on the Aripo Savannahs. It is also a common South American species. In the Aripo Savannahs it sometimes attains densities in excess of 20 plants per square metre. Plants however are extremely short-lived, of a growing season of no more than three months. Typically, the plant measures up to about 40 cm and the inflorescence will bear a few flowers spaced along it.

Habenaria pauciflora

Perhaps one of the most uncommon of the Trinidad orchids is *Habenaria pauciflora*. This species is known in Trinidad only from the St Joseph Savannah above Mount St Benedict. It is known from South America but has only been recorded three times in Trinidad. Although a large species, measuring up to about 80 cm, it produces few flowers.

Habenaria pauciflora

Triphora surinamensis

The minute *Triphora surinamensis* is uncommon but fairly widely distributed in northern South America and in the Lesser Antilles. It is typically a plant of the savannahs and is cleistogamous and grows to a height of about 7 cm.

Triphora surinamensis

Pogonia rosea
(Cleistes rosea)

Pogonia tenuis
(Cleistes tenuis)

Pogonia rosea

This is one of the most handsome of the ground orchids to
be seen in the Aripo Savannahs. The species flowers at the
start of the rainy season and plants are usually found in clumps
and associated with small bushes or shrubs in the open
savannah. The flowers are large and showy but comparatively
short-lived. Height to about 80 cm.

Pogonia tenuis

This is one of the smaller ground orchids found in the
savannah at Aripo. It is far more numerous than *Pogonia rosea*
and appears to favour wetter parts of the savannah. Leaves
are very much reduced and one or two flowers are borne in
the leaf axils. Height to about 12 cm.

21

Vanilla mexicana

Vanilla mexicana

This is one of the very widely distributed *Vanillas* and is certainly the most common one to be seen in Trinidad. It is very easily recognised in the field by its broad papery leaves. It flowers usually in the dry season and several clusters of flowers may be borne simultaneously. The species is particularly common in secondary forests in the Valencia area. Vines may exceed 15 m.

Vanilla phaeantha

This is one of the very widely distributed species occurring in South America, the southern part of USA, the Greater Antilles and the Lesser Antilles. It is however not as common as *Vanilla mexicana* within its range. It is a large species found more frequently in montane forests, readily identified by its large, thick and shiny leaves. Vines may exceed 25 m.

Epistephium parviflorum

This is a common savannah-dwelling orchid of South America. In the Lesser Antilles it is found only in Trinidad in the Aripo Savannahs. It is an extremely showy species with an extended flowering season which may run for most of the year. Large specimens may measure in excess of 1 m.

Vanilla phaeantha

Epistephium parviflorum

Cranichis muscosa

This species is extremely widely distributed in tropical America. It is a smaller, easily missed species found usually associated with wet conditions. Occasionally it may be found beside streams in clusters of dozens of plants. Although minute, the flowers are extremely attractive. Leaves are few, long, petiolate and plants measure up to about 8 cm.

Spiranthes acaulis (Sarcoglottis acaulis)

This is a widely distributed species and has been recorded from South and Central America. It is common in the Lesser Antilles usually in forest environments. It is extremely variable in its vegetative growth and like many *Spiranthes,* it flowers after the leaves wilt at the end of the growing season. Leaf colour varies from green, yellow, spotted green to purple and leaves may measure up to about 25 cm. Inflorescence may measure 50 cm.

Spiranthes costaricencis

While most *Spiranthes* are terrestrial, this species is more frequently epiphytic on horizontal branches, particularly on cocoa. Tuberoids are few, of irregular shape and firmly attached. Height to about 10 cm. Inflorescence to about 25 cm.

Spiranthes cranichoides

This probably is one of the most widely distributed species in the American Tropics. Although small and with insignificant flowers, the vegetative growth is variegated and attractive. It has been widely reported throughout the Lesser Antilles and only recently discovered in Trinidad. Height to about 10 cm.

Cranichis muscosa

Spiranthes acaulis
(*Sarcoglottis acaulis*)

Spiranthes costaricencis

Spiranthes cranichoides

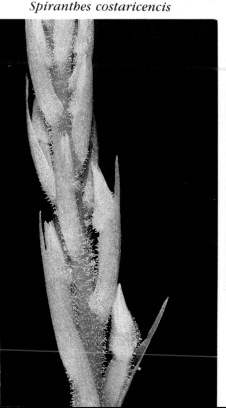

25

Spiranthes lanceolata (Stenorhynchos lanceolata)

Spiranthes simplex

Erythrodes plantaginea

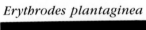

Spiranthes lanceolata (Stenorhynchos lanceolata)

This species like the previous one is also commonly found in the American Tropics. It is particularly common along road cuttings and grows under the harshest of conditions. It too sheds all leaves before flowering. Height to about 15 cm with inflorescence up to about 40 cm.

Spiranthes simplex

This is perhaps the most intriguing of the *Spiranthes* to be found in the Lesser Antilles. The species was first described by Crueger well over 100 years ago. Although several collectors have sought it, it is only recently that it has been recollected in the Aripo Savannahs. It is a minute, short-lived species consisting of essentially nothing more than a spike bearing one or two flowers and a pair of tuberoids. The species is only obvious for a period of about six weeks at the start of the rainy season. It is supposed to be endemic to Trinidad but as Trinidad has been connected to the mainland until comparatively recent times, it has a South American flora and it would not be surprising for this species to be found some day in Venezuela. Other species supposedly endemic to Trinidad have subsequently been found on the South American mainland.

Erythrodes plantaginea

This is a common ground-dwelling orchid found throughout the Lesser Antilles and Greater Antilles. It is rather like a broad-leafed water grass and may easily be confused with members of the Commelinaceae. The inflorescence is a compact mass of minute flowers. Height of plant up to about 40 cm.

Stelis ophioglossoides

EPIDENROIDEAE

Stelis ophioglossoides

The genus *Stelis* is an interesting genus found in South America, Central America and the Antilles. The species are not readily identified in the field because of their minute flowers. One species, *Stelis ophioglossoides* is a common epiphyte in most forests and is particularly common in cocoa plantations. It is usually found in dense mats growing on horizontal branches and may be confused with *Pleurothallis* species. The sepals are usually larger than the petals and the flowers may open and close with changes in the moisture content of the air. Height to about 15 cm.

Pleurothallis acutissima

This is one of the minute *Pleurothallis* species. It is usually associated with the lower levels of the forest where it may be found creeping along smaller branches. In the Lesser Antilles, it is known only from Trinidad. Leaves measure less than 2 cm.

Pleurothallis acutissima

Pleurothallis archidiaconi

Pleurothallis archidiaconi

At one time *Pleurothallis archidiaconi* was thought to be a species endemic to Trinidad. It has however been recorded from Venezuela. The species is easily recognised in the field by the form of the leaf. It is a modest sized plant found in open clumps and the leaves are leathery and heart-shaped. When in bloom, the flower appears to be growing out of the centre of the leaf. The flowers are extremely variable in colouration but the usual colour is yellow. The specimen figured is unusual in having a deep red lip. Height to about 25 cm.

Pleurothallis ciliaris

This is one of the smaller species usually found in the upper storeys in the forest, particularly in moist forest. As with many *Pleurothallis* species, the lip is hinged and vibrates with the slightest air movement. It is possible that this may be related to pollination. Height to about 3 cm.

Pleurothallis ciliata

This is an extremely widely distributed species in Trinidad but it is never found in large mats. It is readily identified in the field by its thick fleshy leaves and, if in flower, by the characteristic yellow flowers. The dorsal sepal is enlarged, while the lateral ones are fused so that flowers are shell-like. Height up to about 12 cm.

Pleurothallis consimilis

This is one of the smaller species found in the lower strata of the forests. It is easily identified in the field by its size and form. The leaves are thick and oval-shaped and it has a creeping growth pattern. Leaves measure up to about 5 cm.

Pleurothallis diffusa

This species of *Pleurothallis* is one of the larger species and is usually found in forests at higher elevations. It is extremely common in the northern range of Trinidad at elevations above 700 metres. Unlike most species, this produces large numbers of flowers. Characteristically it grows in open clumps measuring up to about 30 cm in height.

Pleurothallis ciliaris

Pleurothallis ciliata

Pleurothallis consimilis

Pleurothallis diffusa

Pleurothallis discoidea

Pleurothallis discoidea

This is one of the most common *Pleurothallis* species found in Trinidad. In form it resembles *Pleurothallis diffusa* but is half to a third of the size of the former species. It occurs in clumps frequently inter-growing with *Pleurothallis pruinosa*. It flowers frequently during the year and the flowers are usually single and occasionally paired. The flower is similar in general appearance to that of *Pleurothallis ciliata*. Height to about 12 cm.

Pleurothallis orbicularis

This species is easily recognised in the field by its leaves which are fleshy and almost circular. It is not common in Trinidad but has been found in widely varying habitats, from deep shade to well exposed conditions. Height to about 7 cm.

Pleurothallis polygonoides

Known only from Trinidad, this minute plant produces flowers singly and infrequently. Of special interest is the mobile lip which vibrates with the slightest disturbance.

Pleurothallis orbicularis

Pleurothallis polygonoides

Pleurothallis pruinosa

Octomeria graminifolia

Pleurothallis pruinosa

The most common *Pleurothallis* to be found in the Lesser Antilles is *Pleurothallis pruinosa.* This remarkable little plant is found through much of South America, Central America and the Antilles. Indeed it is probably the first species of orchid that anyone notices when walking through a field of cocoa. It has been recorded from all of the Lesser Antilles except for Barbados. The flowers are few and insignificant. Height to about 7 cm.

Octomeria graminifolia

Easily confused with *Pleurothallis* and *Stelis,* is *Octomeria graminifolia.* This species is minute and usually has a creeping growth pattern. The flowers are minute. Leaves to about 4 cm.

Octomeria grandiflora

Octomeria grandiflora in contrast to *Octomeria graminifolia* is larger and usually found in clumps. It is forest-dwelling and typically leaves are fleshy and their undersides are deep brick-red. Flowers are usually clustered and although small, are extremely showy. Height to about 15 cm.

Octomeria grandiflora

Richenbachanthus reflexus

This is an extremely common species in northern South America and Trinidad. The species is usually associated with large trees. It is very easily identified in the field by its growth form. The leaves are terete and are clustered and hanging. Old specimens are somewhat similar in general appearance to the epiphytic cactus *Rhipsalis*. Although extremely common in Trinidad, it is unusual to see these plants in flower as the flowers are small and inconspicuous. The species has also been recorded from Grenada.

Jaquiniella globosa

Perhaps one of the most common species to be found in the Eastern Caribbean, *Jaquiniella globosa* is easily recognised in the field. It is small but forms tufts of slender stems with sub-terete leaves and is found in lightly shaded conditions.

Epidendrum bradfordii

This species is common in northern South America and Trinidad. Typically the species has a prominent oval pseudobulb bearing a single, narrow and leathery leaf. The species is easily confused with *Epidendrum oncidioides* which has an almost identical growth form. The flowers are of moderate size, numerous and somewhat showy. Height to about 30 cm.

Epidendrum ciliare

This is one of the widely distributed species found throughout the Lesser Antilles. It is extremely variable in form but easily identified when in flower. As with many *Epidendrum* species, the lip is deeply divided and the lateral lobes in this species are typically finely fringed. Flowers are few, large, showy, fragrant and unusually long-lived. Height to about 30 cm.

Richenbachanthus reflexus

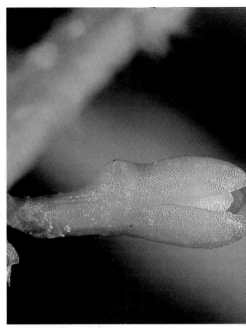

Jacquinella globosa

Epidendrum bradfordii

Epidendrum ciliare

Epidendrum coronatum

The Lamb's Tail orchid is found in northern South America and Trinidad and is one of the largest species of the genus. A mature specimen may measure in excess of 1 m and the stem may be up to about 1.5 cm in thickness. Typically the stem grows horizontally from large trees. When in flower the inflorescence is hanging and as the flowers are white, it gives the form of a lamb's tail. Flowering is during March.

Epidendrum compressum

This is one of the smaller *Epidendrum* species and is not particularly common in Trinidad. It is easily identified however in the field by its stem which is compressed and broadened distally. Flowers are few and small but showy. Although originally thought to be endemic to Trinidad, it has been recorded from Venezuela. Height to about 15 cm.

Epidendrum compressum

Epidendrum coronatum

38

Epidendrum cristatum

Epidendrum cristatum

One of the most handsome members of the genus is *Epidendrum cristatum*. This species is the largest *Epidendrum* species in Trinidad and mature specimens may consist of clumps of 25 to 30 stems with the larger stems measuring more than 1 m. They are easily identified in the field in comparison with the Lamb's Tail orchid, as they grow upwardly inclined and the base of the inflorescence is covered by a series of prominent bracts. This species may flower more than once during the year and there may be more than one inflorescence at a time. The flowers are numerous and showy.

39

Epidendrum fragrans

Epidendrum fragrans

This species is one of the smaller species and is widely distributed in the Lesser Antilles. The pseudobulb is elongate, bearing a single leaf and the plants when mature form dense clumps. The species flowers during the dry season and although each stem bears usually no more than three or four flowers, clumps make a striking display. The flowers, as the name suggests, are extremely fragrant. Height to about 20 cm.

Epidendrum hartii

This species is known from northern South America and Trinidad and Tobago. It is a common species found at higher elevations. It may commonly be seen along the north coast road from Port of Spain to Maracas Bay. It flowers in March but the flowers, while numerous, are not particularly striking. Height to about 50 cm.

Epidendrum hombersleyi

This is an uncommon species thought to be endemic to Trinidad. It is easily identified in the field by the leaves which are acuminate or pointed distally. Height to about 60 cm.

Epidendrum hartii

Epidendrum bombersleyi

Epidendrum ibaguense

Epidendrum ibaguense

This is one of the most spectacular members of the genus to be found in the Lesser Antilles. The form of the plant is sometimes referred to as a reed stem type and when in flower may measure in excess of 1 m. The flowers are borne at the end of a long inflorescence and are moderately large and extremely showy. The plant is not common but certainly widely distributed through northern South America and the Lesser Antilles.

Epidendrum imatophyllum   *Epidendrum latifolium*

Epidendrum imatophyllum

Another uncommon reed stem *Epidendrum* is *Epidendrum imatophyllum*. This species is similar in growth habit to *Epidendrum ibaguense* but the inflorescence is shorter and the flowers are lilac-coloured. Height to about 80 cm.

Epidendrum latifolium

One of the most striking *Epidendrum* species to be found in the Lesser Antilles and in northern South America is *Epidendrum latifolium*. This species was formerly included in *Epidendrum nocturnum* which itself is a complex assembly of related varieties. *Epidendrum latifolium* is a forest-dwelling species more commonly found at higher elevations. It produces a single large white flower at a time during the flowering season which may be extended for several months. The flowers are fragrant. It has been recorded in many of the islands of the Lesser Antilles. It is very easily identified in the field. It is a large plant measuring about up to 50 cm and the stem is flattened distally. Usually there are no more than three or four broad leathery leaves.

Epidendrum nocturnum

This is a common species of northern South America and the Lesser Antilles. It occurs in a variety of forms. A common form in Trinidad is moderately large, clumped and bearing up to a dozen leaves borne alternately on either side of the stem. The stem is generally cylindrical. The flowers are very similar to those of *Epidendrum latifolium*. Height to about 50 cm.

Epidendrum nocturnum var. *minus*

One variety of *Epidendrum nocturnum* commonly found in Trinidad is *Epidendrum nocturnum* var *minus*. This is a small grass-like species about a third the size of the normal *Epidendrum nocturnum* which has been found in a wide range of habitats in Trinidad, frequently with other forms of *Epidendrum nocturnum* and *Epidendrum latifolium*. Height to about 30 cm.

Epidendrum oncidiodes

This species may be easily confused in the field with *Epidendrum bradfordii*. It is possible that the two may be in fact one species. There is a variety called *gravidum* which is cleistogamous and in which the pods have a granular surface. Var. *gravidum* is far more common. Height to about 20 cm.

Epidendrum nocturnum

Epidendrum nocturnum var. *minus*

Epidendrum oncidiodes

Epidendrum ottonis

This small delicate species is widely distributed in northern South America and Trinidad. It is readily identified in the field by its much flattened pseudobulb and its narrow leaves. The flowers are small. Height to about 15 cm.

Epidendrum ramosum

One of the most common *Epidendrum* species of the Lesser Antilles is *Epidendrum ramosum.* It is very easily identified by its peculiar horizontal branching growth form. Its flowers are small and few. Length to about 50 cm.

Epidendrum rigidum

Probably the most common and widely distributed member of the genus is *Epidendrum rigidum.* This species also appears to have a wide range of tolerance. It may be found from sea level in sea blast to the tops of mountains. Flowers are small, enveloped in bracts and green in colour. The species is certainly one of the most commonly seen. Height to about 20 cm.

Epidendrum ottonis

Epidendrum ramosum

Epidendrum rigidum

Epidendrum secundum

Epidendrum stenopetalum (*Dimerandra stenopetala*)

48

Epidendrum secundum

Epidendrum secundum is common on islands such as St Lucia and Dominica when it may be epithytic or lithophytic. It flowers frequently during the year.

Epidendrum stenopetalum
(Dimerandra stenopetala)

One of the most common orchid species to be seen in Trinidad is *Epidendrum stenopetalum*. This species occurs in clumps and the stems are of moderate size up to about 40 cm in length and about the thickness of a pencil. The leaves are small and leathery. The species may be found with *Epidendrum rigidum* and *Epidendrum fragrans* in a wide variety of habitats. Although small, the flowers are very showy. Flowering takes place during October and November and a single flower is produced at a time.

Epidendrum strobiliferum

Another extremely common *Epidendrum* in the Lesser Antilles is the tiny *Epidendrum strobiliferum*. This species is easily recognised in the field by its size and horizontal growth form. Growth form is similar to that of *Epidendrum ramosum* but the plants are about a third the size. Flowers are insignificant. Length to about 15 cm.

Epidendrum strobiliferum

Caularthron bicornutum

In Trinidad one of the most common orchids associated with the seaside is the Virgin orchid *Caularthron bicornutum*. This species grows epiphytically but it also may be found growing in masses on rocks and cliffs near the seashore. They are particularly common on cliffs in the Bocas region and on the headland between Maracas and Tyrico Bays. The plants have large pseudobulbs and basally there is an opening leading into a cavity in which the pseudobulb invariably houses ants. The flowers which are large and showy open in sequence on the inflorescence over a period of about five or six weeks at the end of the dry season. The species is also found inland in forests but not as commonly. The species is also widely distributed in northern South America. The local name given to it, the Virgin orchid, relates to the form of the column which resembles that of a Madonna figure. Height to about 30 cm.

Caularthron bilamellatum

The small Virgin orchid *Caularthron bilamellatum* is common in Trinidad and northern South America. It is quite common on big trees in Port of Spain and around the St Augustine Campus of the University of the West Indies. This species is frequently cleistogamous but occasionally in very dry seasons it flowers normally. Height to about 20 cm.

Caularthron bicornutum

Caularthron bilamellatum

Cattleya deckeri   *Schomburgkia gloriosa*

Cattleya deckeri

Trinidad has one species of *Cattleya*. It is common in the Northern Range but unfortunately the local species is cleistogamous. Occasionally in hard dry seasons the flowers will partially open before they are fertilised. The typical growth form is that of the *Cattleya* genus. Height to about 30 cm.

Schomburgkia gloriosa

In the Lesser Antilles there will be found growing in cultivation, or in wild conditions, more than one species of *Schomburgkia*. In Trinidad three species are listed but one of these is almost certainly an introduced species. The most common species in Trinidad is *Schomburgkia gloriosa* which has not been previously recorded from Trinidad. The species is extremely common in south-west Trinidad and in most of the Northern Range valleys. Large populations have been noted in Caura Valley, Maracas Valley and Santa Cruz. This species locally is mostly cleistogamous but occasionally in hard dry seasons the flowers open normally. The *Schomburgkia* species of the Windward and Leeward Islands are all thought to be introduced hybrid species not native to the islands. Height to about 50 cm. Flower stalk to about 2 m.

51

Brassavola cucullata

One of the most striking orchids of the Lesser Antilles is *Brassavola cucullata*. This species is widely distributed in the American tropics and is very easily identified in the field. It usually grows epiphytically from tree trunks and leaves are clumped and terete. The flowers are single, large, showy and fragrant and plants appear to produce flowers continuously throughout the year. The species appears to have an extreme tolerance to desiccation. In Trinidad the species has been seen in the north-western peninsula and at Maracas Bay but never in the numbers that may be seen in the Leeward and Windward Islands. In Grenada for example, it is not uncommon to find this as a dominant orchid species on a tree. Height to about 20 cm.

Scaphyglottis fusiformis

This a common species in Trinidad and northern South America. It is of interest particularly for its growth form. The stem becomes swollen mesially at the end of the growing period and a new stem appears distally. The appearance is of a chain of ribbed pseudobulbs. The species is common in wet forests. Height to about 20 cm.

Scaphyglottis modesta (Hexadesmia modesta)

This is a widely distributed species found throughout the American tropics. Its growth form is of interest. The stem produces one or two leaves at the end of a growing period and becomes slightly swollen. This growth pattern is repeated so that a specimen may appear superficially branched. The flowers are usually single and much enclosed by bracts and open only slightly. The species flowers frequently during the rainy season. Height to about 40 cm.

Brassavola cucullata

Scaphyglottis fusiformis

Scaphyglottis modesta (Hexadesmia modesta)

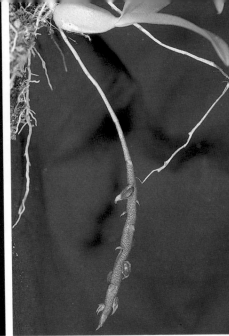

Polystachya concreta

Bulbophyllum pachyrachis

Eulophia alta

Cyrtopodium parviflorum

Polystachya concreta

This is an extremely widely distributed species in the American tropics and its distribution is pan-tropical. It is an extremely hardy species which produces an elongate inflorescence with insignificant, cream or pale green flowers. One of the most common species in the Lesser Antilles and may be found in both exposed and forested environments. Height commonly to about 20 cm but occasionally much larger specimens may be found.

Bulbophyllum pachyrachis

The Rat's Tail orchid is a common species in northern South America and Trinidad. The distinctive feature of this species is that the inflorescence which is pendulous is much swollen when in bloom. It is possible that the swollen inflorescence may be an accessory water store. Height to about 15 cm.

Eulophia alta

This species is of wide distribution in the American tropics. It is a large terrestrial plant which may attain a height in excess of 1 m. The inflorescence may be in excess of 2 m. This species, although widely distributed, is never really common. It does not have pseudobulbs but the base of the leaves becomes swollen to form onion-like corms. A mature specimen may produce in excess of 60 flowers.

Cyrtopodium parviflorum

One of the unusual ground orchids of the Aripo Savannahs and similar savannahs in northern South America is *Cyrtopodium parviflorum*. This species is now found only in the Aripo Savannahs and the numbers of specimens have been considerably reduced because of fires and over-collecting. The Trinidad and Tobago Field Naturalists' Club has done a study on the general biology of this species. Height to about 40 cm.

Catasetum cristatum

There are two species of *Catasetum* in Trinidad. *Catasetum cristatum* is the less common one. It is distributed widely in Trinidad particularly in forested areas. Unlike the other *Catasetum* species, the flowers are perfect. Little is known about the pollination of this species. Height to about 20 cm.

Catasetum macrocarpum

One of the most prominent orchids to be seen on large trees and telephone poles around Port of Spain is the Monk's Head orchid, *Catasetum macrocarpum*. This species, as the name suggests, produces an extremely large seed pod. It has pseudobulbs which measure up to about 30 cm by 6 cm. The leaves are papery and strongly veined. What is intriguing about the species is that the flowers may be either male or female or occasionally perfect. Occasionally also one flower stalk may bear both male and female flowers. *Catasetum macrocarpum* is pollinated by euglossine bees, *Eulaema*. The male flowers have a very complex trigger mechanism which when activated will eject the pollinia which become attached by the viscidium to the thorax of the bee. The name Monk's Head is derived from the appearance of the inverted lip of the male flower.

Paphinia cristata

One very much sought after orchid in Trinidad is *Paphinia cristata*. This extremely showy orchid is not uncommon but distribution tends to be clumped. There are parts of Trinidad where it is possible to find several hundred specimens within an area of one hectare.

The plant is clumped with flattened ovoid pseudobulbs and papery, veined leaves. One or two large showy flowers are produced usually in August. Height to about 20 cm.

Catasetum cristatum

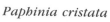

Catasetum macrocarpum ♂

Catasetum macrocarpum ♀

Paphinia cristata

Stanhopea grandiflora

This is a tropical American species of wide distribution being found throughout northern South America and in Central America. Vegetatively the plant consists of an ovoid pseudobulb surrounded by bracts and a single multi-veined papery leaf. A mature specimen may measure about 50 cm. This species produces usually two large, fragrant but very short-lived flowers. As in the case of *Catasetum* the pollination is by euglossine bees.

Gongora quinquinervis

The Jack Spaniard orchid, *Gongora quinquinervis* is an extremely common plant found in secondary forest. It is very easily recognised in the field by its fluted pseudobulb and its paired leaves. Its inflorescence is elongate and pendulous, bearing up to about 50 flowers. The local name relates to its rough resemblance to the paper wasp *Polistes*. In the Trinidad flora it has been listed as two separate species but clearly there is only one variable species. The common form is mottled but there are deep red varieties and pale yellow to white varieties. Pollination is by the bee *Euglossa*. Height to about 40 cm.

Stanhopea grandiflora   *Gongora quinquinervis*

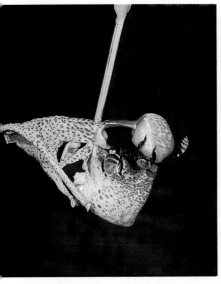

Coryanthes macrantha   *Coryanthes speciosa*

Coryanthes macrantha

Perhaps the most spectacular of the Trinidad orchids is the Monkey Throat orchid, *Coryanthes macrantha*. In this species the vegetative growth bears a superficial resemblance to that of the Jack Spaniard orchid. The pseudobulb however is longer and bears a large number of ridges. The leaves are multi-veined and slightly leathery. What is of particular interest in the species is that it produces, at a time, only one extremely large and bizarre flower which is pollinated by the bee *Eulaema*. Darwin in his book on orchid pollination described the pollination of this species. The name Monkey Throat relates to the fancied resemblance of the lip of the orchid to the larynx of the Red Howler Monkey.

Coryanthes speciosa

This species is generally smaller than *Coryanthes macrantha* and cannot really be differentiated vegetatively in the field. It however produces a few smaller flowers of the same general form. It too is pollinated by euglossine bees. Height to about 30 cm.

59

Xylobium colleyi

Bifrenaria aurantiaca

Xylobium colleyi

The Goat's Head orchid gets its name presumably from its offensive smell. It has the same general form as *Stanhopea* but has a longer petiole. A cluster of foul smelling flowers resembling rotting meat is borne basally. The flowers attract carrion flies which are presumably their pollinators. Height to about 50 cm.

Bifrenaria aurantiaca

Some of the most attractive orchids lack common names. One such is *Bifrenaria aurantiaca*. This species is found in northern South America and Trinidad, but in Trinidad it is not common. It produces an elongate flower stalk with many small, but attractive flowers. Height to about 25 cm.

Bifrenaria longicornis

This is an uncommon species in Trinidad although it is widely reported in northern South America. In Trinidad it is not uncommon in secondary forests around the Aripo Savannahs. A mature specimen will consist of an elongate stem, interspersed with pseudobulbs and may extend from the forest floor up to the canopy. This species appears to be able to take extreme exposure. Height of pseudobulb and leaf to about 25 cm.

Bifrenaria longicornis

Koellenstenia graminea

This is a small and peculiar grass-like plant found epiphytically in forests usually in deep shade. Although a tiny plant, it produces extremely showy flowers. Height to about 15 cm.

Aganisia pulchella

Aganisia pulchella has a small creeping form and is sometimes found terrestrially but more frequently epiphytically in secondary forests around the Aripo Savannahs. Some authorities suggest that this is just another variety of a savannah-dwelling form, *Otostylis*. Height to about 20 cm.

Otostylis brachystalix

In the dry season one of the most striking sights in the Aripo Savannahs is the Aripo ground orchid, *Otostylis brachystalix*. This species is grass-like in form with a small pseudobulb and produces an erect inflorescence with moderate size, showy, white flowers. Height to about 50 cm.

Koellenstenia graminea   *Aganisia pulchella*

Otostylis brachystalix   *Stenia pallida*

Stenia pallida

This is a common epiphyte of cocoa. A mature plant consists of a clump of non-petiolate leaves and in the flowering season produces single pendulous and extremely pale, cream flowers. Height to about 20 cm.

Maxillaria alba

Maxillaria alba is an uncommon species in Trinidad found at higher elevations in the upper canopy. For this reason, it is not commonly encountered except on fallen trees. The stem is elongate and covered with numerous bracts. Height to about 20 cm but older plants form larger tangles.

Maxillaria alba

Maxillaria brachybulbon

Maxillaria camaridii

Maxillaria brachybulbon

This is a tiny *Maxillaria* species which has only recently been recorded in Trinidad. It is a common species in northern South America. Height to about 7 cm.

Maxillaria camaridii

One of the larger members of the genus and certainly one of the most common in Trinidad is *Maxillaria camaridii*. This species has an elongate stem covered with bracts and pseudobulbs, laterally placed. Clusters of a few flowers are produced periodically in the leaf axil. Flowers are large, white, showy but very short-lived. This species has also been recorded in Grenada. Height to about 30 cm but a mature specimen will form a massive pendulous tangle.

Maxillaria conferta

This is a small *Maxillaria* species widely distributed in northern South America, Trinidad and the Lesser Antilles generally. It is a common inhabitant of cocoa. It produces clusters of small white flowers enveloped in bracts. Height to about 15 cm. Plants may be clumped when old.

Maxillaria conferta

Maxillaria discolor

This species is known in Trinidad from one specimen collected in the Northern Range. A mature plant consists of a cluster of large, very much flattened pseudobulbs and flowers are single and from the leaf axil. The species is well known in northern South America. Height to about 25 cm.

Maxillaria guareimensis

The largest species of *Maxillaria* in Trinidad has only recently been recorded. This is *Maxillaria guareimensis*. This species is in fact quite common but as it appears to prefer growing in the upper canopy in large trees and, as it has the same general growth form as *Maxillaria camaridii*, it clearly has been missed by earlier collectors. Flowers are solitary and in the leaf axil. Flowering is during the wet season from August through to December.

Maxillaria discolor   *Maxillaria guareimensis*

Maxillaria ringens

Maxillaria ringens

A common *Maxillaria* of wet forest in Trinidad is *Maxillaria ringens*. The species is very similar to the common *Maxillaria rufescens* in growth form but the leaves are long-petiolate. Flowers are single, yellow and long-stalked. Height to about 30 cm. It is also known under the synonym *M. trinitatis*.

Maxillaria rufescens

The most common *Maxillaria* in Trinidad is clearly *Maxillaria rufescens*. Mature specimens consist of clusters of elongate, somewhat flattened pseudobulbs each with a single leaf. The flowers are single or occasionally paired and are borne basally. Flowers are yellow to orange with red spotting and are fragrant. Height to about 25 cm.

Maxillaria rufescens

Ionopsis satyrioides

Ionopsis satyrioides

A common epiphyte in the Lesser Antilles is the tiny *Ionopsis satyrioides*. There are two species of *Ionopsis* in the Lesser Antilles and this species is readily recognised in the field by the terete leaves. The flower stalk is delicately branched and a few lilac coloured flowers are borne. Height to about 10 cm. Flower stalk to about 20 cm.

Ionopsis utricularioides

This is an extremely common epiphyte in the Eastern Caribbean. Although common, it tends to occur in clumps. Sometimes one tree will have several hundreds of plants on it and these will be the only specimens in the immediate area. The plants are tiny, usually with maroon pigmented leaves and have an elongate and very delicate flower stalk bearing large numbers of minute lilac coloured flowers. Height to about 8 cm. Flower stalk to about 35 cm.

Ionopsis utricularioides

*Rodriguezia
lanceolata*

Rodriguezia lanceolata

The Coral orchid is an extremely common epiphyte of cocoa
and citrus in Trinidad. It is known also from Grenada. These
small plants measure up to about 15 cm and produce a pair
of inflorescences with small showy flowers. They make a
striking contrast in a citrus orchard in May when they come
into bloom.

Trizeuxis falcata

This is one of the most common native orchids of Trinidad.
It does not however have a local name, particularly because
of its size and its extremely tiny flowers. It is a common
inhabitant of citrus and may on occasions even be found
growing epiphytically on leaves of other plants. Height to
about 8 cm.

Trizeuxis falcata

Aspasia variegata

Brassia caudata

Leochilus labiatus

Oncidium altissimum

Aspasia variegata

This is an uncommon, moderate size plant easily distinguished by its extremely flat pseudobulb. Its flower is single and basal and extremely showy.

Brassia caudata

One of the most striking epiphytic orchids to be found in Trinidad is the Spider orchid, *Brassia caudata*. The species is widely distributed but not particularly common. It is a forest-dwelling species. The inflorescence is produced basally and it bears up to about a dozen extremely large flowers. Height to about 35 cm.

Leochilus labiatus

The tiny *Leochilus labiatus* is found widely distributed in tropical America but it is not particularly numerous. This tiny plant produces a pair of minute but strikingly handsome flowers. Height to about 5 cm.

Oncidium altissimum

All of the *Oncidium* species have common names in Trinidad and one of the most common is *Oncidium altissimum,* the Brown Bee orchid. This species has a reduced pseudobulb, large fleshy spear-shaped leaves and measures up to about 70 cm. If exposed to the sun, the leaves are red spotted. The inflorescence is borne basally and in a mature specimen may measure up to about 3 m. It is the one orchid species that one is likely to see in people's gardens in the country. It has a wide distribution in the American tropics.

Oncidium
ampliatum

Oncidium ampliatum

The Yellow Bee orchid, *Oncidium ampliatum,* is rare in Trinidad and very much sought after by collectors. It has a flattened pseudobulb with a single leathery leaf and produces a spray of brilliant yellow flowers. It is known from northern South America. Height to about 30 cm.

Oncidium cebolleta

The Yellow Bee orchid was probably introduced into Trinidad from Venezuela where it is common. In Trinidad it is known mainly from large trees in Port of Spain. It is also recorded from several of the islands of the Lesser Antilles. It is possible that its distribution may be through human activity. Leaves are terete and measure up to about 50 cm.

Oncidium citrinum

Oncidium citrinum is an uncommon Bee Orchid found mainly at high elevations in Trinidad. The pseudobulbs are elongate and ridged. One of the remarkable features of this Bee orchid is that its flower stalk may take between six and nine months to grow to the point where it produces flowers. The flower stalk frequently, however, aborts or produces few flowers. Mature specimens, however, occasionally produce long sprays measuring up to about 2 m of striking yellow flowers. Height of plant to about 30 cm.

Oncidium cebolleta

Oncidium haematochilum

Orchids frequently form natural hybrids. An uncommon naturally occurring hybrid is *Oncidium haematochilum* which is a hybrid between *Oncidium altissimum* and *Oncidium lanceanum*.

Oncidum citrinum

Oncidium haematochilum

73

Oncidium lanceanum

The Cedros Bee orchid, *Oncidium lanceanum,* is probably the most sought after native orchid of Trinidad and fetches high prices. The species appears to be confined to the south-western peninsula of Trinidad but the species is of wide distribution in northern South America. Pseudobulbs are reduced and bear a single broad, leathery leaf which is normally red spotted. Plants produce one or two flower stalks simultaneously and each will have up to about a dozen large, showy, long-lived and extremely fragrant flowers. Height to about 35 cm.

Oncidium papilio

The Butterfly orchid is a common species in northern South America and in Trinidad. It has almost certainly been over-collected in Trinidad for export. Mature plants will consist of a number of flattened pseudobulbs each bearing a leathery leaf with, almost invariably, a fine red tracery. The flower stalks are elongate up to about 1 m and produce solitary flowers in sequence. A flower stalk may in fact continue to produce flowers over extended periods, possibly up to about three years. The individual flowers are large and extremely showy and resemble a butterfly. Height to about 25 cm.

Oeceoclades maculata

This is a terrestrial orchid which is known from northern South America and has recently been reported in Trinidad. It is common in the islands between Trinidad and Venezuela as well as on the north-western peninsula. It is known also from south-western Trinidad. The leaves are single and variegated. The inflorescence is erect, bearing a cluster of small attractive flowers. This species is found also in Africa. Height to about 25 cm.

Lockhartia acuta

Named for David Lockhart who was curator of the Royal Botanic Gardens in Port of Spain, this rare orchid displays a distinctive vegetative growth form of leaves which are reduced to thick overlapping bracts.

Oncidium lanceanum

Oncidium papilio

Oeceoclades maculata

Lockhartia acuta

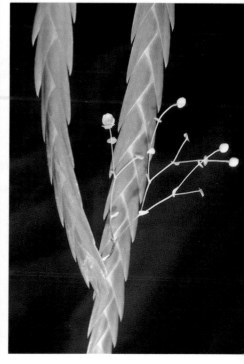

Psygmorchis pusilla

Psygmorchis pusilla

This is a minute plant with leaves arranged in the form of a fan. The plants grow epiphytically on small branches and they are not uncommon on coffee. The distribution of this species is usually clumped and when one plant is found it is likely that several hundreds will be in the general area. It is also probably one of the most difficult plants to grow in captivity. It produces single, showy, yellow flowers from the axils of the leaves. The lip of the flower is uppermost in this species. Height to about 5 cm.

Ornithocephalus gladiatus

This is a common epiphyte with the same general vegetative form as *Psygmorchis pusilla* and *Trizeuxis falcata*. It produces short flower stalks with tiny flowers of bizarre form. The pods are also ornate. As the name suggests, the flowers have the form of the head of a bird. Height to about 5 cm.

Notylia angustifolia

This tiny plant *Notylia angustifolia* is extremely common and widely distributed in Trinidad. The entire plant including the flowers measures no more than about 5 cm in height.

Ornithocephalus gladiatus

Notylia punctata

A less common *Notylia* is *Notylia punctata* which is found in the upper canopy in forests. Its form is essentially the same as the other *Notylia* in Trinidad but its inflorescence is many-flowered and the flowers are larger. Height to about 10 cm with inflorescence of about 20 cm.

Notylia angustifolia   *Notylia punctata*

Cryptarrhena lunata

This species is uncommon in Trinidad. It is a small plant with a pendulous inflorescence, bearing many yellow flowers. The lip is very much modified into a crescent shape reminiscent of a crescent moon. This species is known from northern South America. Height to about 10 cm.

Macradenia lutescens

This is an uncommon species in Trinidad but is known from northern South America. It is a forest dwelling species. Height to about 10 cm.

Dichaea picta

In the Lesser Antilles there is a large number of small to minute epiphytic orchids in the genus *Dichaea*. The systematic status of some of these species is still uncertain. *Dichaea picta* is an extremely common species in Trinidad found usually in deep shade. Flowers are small, single and axillary. Height to about 10 cm.

Campylocentrum micranthum

This is a common species of the Lesser Antilles. It is usually found growing horizontally in shade and generally only loosely attached to the host tree or branch. The inflorescence is short, bearing two rows of tiny pale pink to white flowers. Height to about 30 cm.

Cryptarrhena lunata

Macradenia lutescens

Dichaea picta

Campylocentrum micranthum

Glossary

Anther   The part of the stamen, the male reproductive structure, which bears the pollen.

Bilateral symmetry   The organisational symmetry of an organism which may be divided into right and left halves or mirror images.

Cleistogamous   Self fertilising and non-opening.

Corm   A bulb-like subterranean storage organ.

Column   A unique structure formed of the fusion of the male and female reproductive parts, found only in the Orchidaceae. The column is also known as the gynandrium.

Dimorphic   Occurring in two different forms.

Dioecious   The condition where the male and female parts are produced on different individual plants.

Distal   At the far end of a structure.

Epiphytic   Growing on other plants but not deriving nourishment from the host plant.

Euglossine bee   Members of a sub-family of the Apidae which pollinate certain sub-families of orchids. The bees are attracted by chemical attractants.

Filament   A thread-like structure supporting the anther.

Gynandrium   The column.

Inflorescence   The flower cluster of a plant.

Labellum   The dorsal petal which is different from the other two petals. In most orchids when the flower bud forms it rotates through 180° so that the dorsal petal assumes a ventral position.

Lip   The labellum.

Lithophytic   Living on stone or rock.

Monoecious   The condition where a species produces both male and female parts on the same plant.

Monopodial   A growth pattern which is continuous without branching. In this pattern, growth may be arrested during periods of drought.

Mesial   In the middle region.

Ovary   That part of the pistil or female reproductive structure which bears ovules which become seeds after the process of fertilisation is completed.

Ovule   The part of the ovary which becomes seed on fertilisation.

Perianth   The two clusters of accessory structures which form an envelope about the reproductive structures. There are sepals which are outermost and petals which are innermost.

Petal The inner accessory structure of a flower. In orchids the dorsal one becomes modified into a lip or labellum.

Petiole The stalk of a leaf.

Pistil The female reproductive structure consisting of ovary, style and stigma.

Polymorphic Occurring in several different forms.

Pollinium A mass of pollen.

Proximal Near the base of a structure.

Pseudobulb The swollen stem of an orchid.

Raceme An unbranched flower stalk with stalked flowers.

Rhizome An underground stem.

Rostellum A small beak-like structure derived from one of the stigmata employed in fastening pollen to pollinators of many orchids.

Saprophytic Living on dead material.

Sepal The outer accessory structure forming the envelope around the reproductive structures. In orchids sepals frequently resemble petals in colour and markings.

Spike An unbranched flower stalk with flowers which are not stalked.

Stamen The male reproductive parts of a flower consisting of filament and anther which bears pollen.

Stem The leaf-bearing axis of a plant.

Stigma The part of the female reproductive part of the flower which receives the pollen.

Spur An elongate outgrowth of the lip of *Habenaria* which probably produces nectar.

Style The part of the female reproductive part of a flower between the stigma and the ovaries.

Sympodial A seasonal growth pattern producing apical growth with a lateral bud for the season following.

Terete Circular in cross-section.

Velamen The white or sometimes red or green spongy outer layer of the orchid root which serves as an attachment and for water storage. The velamen may sometimes contain chlorophyll.

Viscidium A gluey adhesive mass which is used to stick the pollen to pollinators, for example in *Catasetum* or *Coryanthes*.

Trimerous Occurring in series of three.

Trimorphic Occurring in three different forms.

Tuberoid A swollen root which serves as a storage organ.

Zygomorphic Having a bilateral symmetry.

Appendix

The listing below is based largely on those of Schultes (1960) and Howard (1974). In the case of the Trinidad listing some names have been amended in accordance with Dunsterville and Garay (1979). The abbreviations in the first column give the general distribution as follows; SA (South America), CA (Central America), NA (North America), GA (Greater Antilles). While there are probably no endemic species in Trinidad there are several in the Windward and Leeward Islands and these are indicated with the letter E. In the case of Trinidad species listed as endemic by Schultes a few are noted with the character E?. Doubtful records have been eliminated where possible and several new records have been added for Trinidad.

CYPRIPEDIOIDEAE	Dist.	Trin.	East Carib.
Selenepedium palmifolium	SA	+	−

ORCHIDOIDEAE

Habenaria alata	SA, CA, GA	+	+
Habenaria eustachya	CA, GA	−	+
Habenaria odontopetala	CA, NA, GA	−	+
Habenaria dussii	GA	−	+
Habenaria monorrhiza	SA, CA, GA	+	+
Habenaria leprieurii	SA	+	−
Habenaria lebrieurii var *heptadactyla*	SA	+	−
Habenaria mesodactyla	SA	+	−
Habenaria pauciflora	SA, CA	+	−
Habenaria repens	SA, CA, NA, GA	+	−

NEOTTIOIDEAE

Triphora surinamensis	SA	+	+
Pogonia grandiflora	SA	+	−
Pogonia rosea	SA	+	−
Pogonia tenuis	SA	+	−
Psilochilus macrophyllus	SA, CA	+	+

82

NEOTTIOIDEAE *(Contd.)*	Dist.	Trin.	East Carib.
Vanilla bartii	E	+	+
Vanilla mexicana	SA, CA, GA	+	+
Vanilla phaeantha	NA, GA	+	+
Vanilla planifolia	CA, GA	−	+
Vanilla pleei	E	−	+
Vanilla pompona	SA, CA	+	+
Vanilla wrightii	SA, GA	+	+
Epistephium parviflorum	SA	+	−
Epistephium ellipticum	SA	+	−
Elleanthus caravata	SA	−	+
Elleanthus cephalotus	SA	+	+
Elleanthus dussii	E	−	+
Elleanthus longibracteata	SA, CA, GA	−	+
Palmorchis pubescens	SA	+	−
Wullschlaegelia aphylla	SA, CA, GA	+	+
Prescottia oligantha	SA, CA, GA	−	+
Prescottia stachyodes	SA, CA, GA	+	+
Pseudocentrum guadalupense	E	−	+
Cranichis muscosa	SA, CA, NA, GA	+	+
Cranichis ovata	GA	−	+
Ponthieva petiolata	GA	−	+
Ponthieva racemosa	SA, CA, NA, GA	−	+
Spiranthes acaulis	SA, CA	+	+
Spiranthes adnata	SA, CA, GA	−	+
Spiranthes cranichoides	SA, CA, NA, GA	+	+
Spiranthes costaricencis	CA, GA	+	−
Spiranthes elata	SA, CA, NA, GA	+	+
Spiranthes grisenbachii	SA	+	−
Spiranthes guayanensis	SA, CA	+	−
Spiranthes lanceolata	SA, CA, NA, GA	+	+
Spiranthes polyantha	CA, NA, GA	−	+
Spiranthes scropulariae	SA	+	−
Spiranthes simplex	E?	+	−
Spiranthes torta	NA, GA	+	+
Eltroplectris calcarata	SA, NA, GA	−	+
Erythrodes hirtella	GA	+	+
Erythrodes plantaginea	GA	+	+
Erythrodes querceticola	SA, CA, NA, GA	−	+
Erythrodes schultesiana	E?	+	−
Erythrodes trinitatis	E?	+	−
Corymborkis corymbosa	SA, CA, GA	−	+

EPIDENDROIDEAE	Dist.	Trin.	East Carib.
Stelis dussii	E	–	+
Stelis muscifera	SA	+	–
Stelis ophioglossoides	SA	+	+
Stelis perpusilliflora	GA	+	+
Stelis pygmaea	GA	–	+
Stelis scabrida	E	–	+
Pleurothallis acutissima	SA	+	–
Pleurothallis archidiaconi	SA	+	–
Pleurothallis aristata	SA, CA, GA	–	+
Pleurothallis ciliaris	SA, CA	+	–
Pleurothallis ciliata	SA	+	–
Pleurothallis consimilis	SA	+	–
Pleurothallis domingensis	GA	–	+
Pleurothallis diffusa	SA	+	–
Pleurothallis discoidea	SA	+	–
Pleurothallis dussii	GA	–	+
Pleurothallis foliata	SA, CA, GA	+	+
Pleurothallis imraei	SA, CA, GA	–	+
Pleurothallis mazei	GA	–	+
Pleurothallis memor	SA, CA	+	+
Pleurothallis ophioglossoides	E	–	+
Pleurothallis orbicularis	SA	+	–
Pleurothallis ovalifolia	SA	+	–
Pleurothallis polygonoides	SA	+	–
Pleurothallis pruinosa	SA, CA, GA	+	+
Pleurothallis ruscifolia	SA, CA, GA	+	+
Pleurothallis sicaria	SA	+	–
Pleurothallis testaefolium	GA	–	+
Pleurothallis velaticaulis	SA, CA	+	–
Pleurothallis wilsoni	GA	–	+
Lepanthes aurea	E	–	+
Lepanthes dussii	E	–	+
Brachionidium dussii	E	–	+
Brachionidium parvum	SA	–	+
Brachionidium sherringii	GA	–	+
Octomeria apiculata	SA	–	+
Octomeria graminifolia	E	+	+
Octomeria grandiflora	SA	+	–
Octomeria tridentata	SA	+	–
Malaxis major	GA	–	+
Malaxis massonii	GA	+	+
Malaxis umbelliflora	GA	+	+
Liparis nervosa	SA, CA	+	+
Liparis vexillefera	SA, CA	+	–
Richenbachanthus reflexus	SA	+	+

84

EPIDENDROIDEAE *(Contd.)*	Dist.	Trin.	East Carib.
Jacquiniella globosa	SA, CA, GA	+	+
Jacquiniella teretifolia	SA, CA, GA	−	+
Epidendrum bradfordii	SA	+	−
Epidendrum ciliare	SA, CA, GA	+	+
Epidendrum coronatum	SA, CA	+	−
Epidendrum cochleatum	SA, CA, NA, GA	−	+
Epidendrum compressum	SA	+	−
Epidendrum crassilabium	SA, CA, GA	+	−
Epidendrum cristatum	SA, CA	+	−
Epidendrum dendrobioides	SA, GA	−	+
Epidendrum difforme	SA, CA, NA, GA	+	+
Epidendrum discoidale	E	−	+
Epidendrum elongatum	SA, CA, GA	+	+
Epidendrum fragrans	SA, CA, GA	+	+
Epidendrum fusiforme	E?	+	−
Epidendrum hartii	SA	+	−
Epidendrum hombersleyi	E?	+	−
Epidendrum ibaguense var *confluens*	SA, CA, GA	+	+
Epidendrum ibaguense var *schomburgkii*	SA	+	−
Epidendrum imatophyllum	SA, CA	+	−
Epidendrum jamaicense	GA	−	+
Epidendrum kraenzlinii	GA	−	+
Epidendrum latifolium	SA, GA	+	+
Epidendrum miserrimum	SA, CA, GA	−	+
Epidendrum lechleri	SA, CA, GA	−	+
Epidendrum mutelianum	E	−	+
Epidendrum nocturnum	SA, CA, NA, GA	+	+
Epidendrum nocturnum var *minus*	SA	+	−
Epidendrum oncidioides	SA, CA	+	−
Epidendrum oncidioides var *gravidum*	SA, CA	+	−
Epidendrum ottonis	SA	+	−
Epidendrum pallidiflorum	GA	−	+
Epidendrum patens	E	−	+
Epidendrum pseudoramosum	SA, CA, GA	−	+
Epidendrum pygmaeum	SA, CA, NA, GA	+	−
Epidendrum ramosum	SA, CA, GA	+	+
Epidendrum rigidum	SA, CA, NA, GA	+	+
Epidendrum schlecterianum	SA, CA	+	−
Epidendrum secundum	SA, CA, NA, GA	+	+
Epidendrum stenopetalum	SA, CA, GA	+	−
Epidendrum strobiliferum	SA, CA, NA, GA	+	+
Epidendrum tipuloideum	SA	+	−
Epidendrum vincentinum	SA, CA, GA	+	+
Epidendrum yatapuense	SA	+	−

EPIDENDROIDEAE *(Contd.)*	Dist.	Trin.	East Carib.
Caularthron bicornutum	SA	+	−
Caularthron bilamellatum	SA, CA	+	−
Tetramicra canaliculata	NA, GA	+	+
Cattleya deckeri	SA, CA	+	−
Schomburgkia gloriosa	SA	+	−
Schomburgkia thompsoniana	SA	+	−
Schomburgkia undulata	SA	+	−
Brassavola cucullata	SA, CA, GA	+	+
Isochilus linearis	SA, CA, GA	+	+
Helleriella punctulata	SA, GA	−	+
Scaphyglottis fusiformis	SA	+	−
Scaphyglottis modesta	SA, GA	+	+
Scaphyglottis prolifera	SA, CA	+	+
Hexadesmia dunstervillei	SA	−	+
Polystachya concreta	Pantropical	+	+
Polystachya foliosa	SA, CA, GA	+	+
Bletia patula	SA, GA	+	+
Bulbophyllum pachyrachis	SA, CA, GA	+	−
Eulophia alta	SA, CA, NA, GA	+	+
Cyrtopodium andersonii	SA	+	+
Cyrtopodium parviflorum	SA	+	−
Cyrtopodium punctatum	SA, CA, NA	+	−
Catasetum cristatum	SA	+	−
Catasetum macrocarpum	SA	+	−
Kegeliella houtteana	SA, CA, GA	+	−
Peristeria cerina	SA	+	−
Peristeria pendula	SA, CA	+	−
Paphinia cristata	SA	+	−
Stanhopea grandiflora	SA	+	−
Gongora quinquinervis	SA, CA	+	−
Coryanthes macrantha	SA	+	−
Coryanthes speciosa	SA, CA	+	−
Xylobium colleyi	SA	+	−
Xylobium pallidiflorum	SA	+	+
Bifrenaria aurantiaca	SA, CA	+	−
Bifrenaria longicornis	SA	+	−

EPIDENDROIDEAE *(Contd.)*	Dist.	Trin.	East Carib.
Koellenstenia graminea	SA	+	−
Aganisia pulchella	SA	+	−
Otostylis brachystalix	SA	+	−
Batemania colleyi	SA	+	−
Stenia pallida	SA	+	−
Cochleanthes flabelliformis	SA	+	−
Cochleanthes trinitatis	E?	+	−
Huntleya lucida	SA	+	−
Huntleya meleagris	SA	+	−
Maxillaria alba	SA, CA	+	−
Maxillaria albiflora	E?	+	−
Maxillaria arachnites	SA	+	−
Maxillaria brachybulbon	SA	+	−
Maxillaria broadwayi	E?	+	−
Maxillaria camaridii	SA	+	−
Maxillaria coccinea	SA	+	+
Maxillaria conferta	SA	+	+
Maxillaria discolor	SA	+	−
Maxillaria guadalupensis	SA	−	+
Maxillaria guareimensis	SA	+	−
Maxillaria inflexa	GA	−	+
Maxillaria liparophylla	SA	+	−
Maxillaria meridensis	SA	−	+
Maxillaria reichenheimana	SA, CA	+	−
Maxillaria ringens	SA	+	−
Maxillaria rufescens	SA, CA	+	−
Maxillaria variabilis	SA, CA	+	−
Ionopsis satyrioides	SA, GA	+	+
Ionopsis utricularioides	SA, GA	+	+
Rodriguezia lanceolata	SA, CA, GA	+	+
Trizeuxis falcata	SA, CA	+	−
Quekettia pygamea	SA	+	−
Aspasia variegata	SA	+	−
Trichopilia mutica	SA	+	−
Trichopilia subulata	SA	+	−
Brassia caudata	SA, CA, NA, GA	+	−
Leochilus labiatus	SA, CA, GA	+	−
Leochilus scriptus	CA, GA	+	−
Oncidium altissimum	SA, CA, NA, GA	+	+
Oncidium ampliatum	SA, CA	+	−

87

EPIDENDROIDEAE *(Contd.)*	Dist.	Trin.	East Carib.
Oncidium cebolleta	SA, CA, NA, GA	+	+
Oncidium citrinum	SA	+	–
Oncidium haematochilum	SA	+	–
Oncidium jaquinianum	E	–	+
Oncidium lanceanum	SA	+	–
Oncidium leiboldii	GA	–	+
Oncidium meirax	SA, GA	–	+
Oncidium papilio	SA	+	–
Oncidium picturatum	SA	–	+
Oncidium urophyllum	E	–	+
Oncidium wydleri	GA	–	+
Oeceoclades maculata	SA	+	–
Psygmorchis pusilla	SA	+	–
Lockhartia acuta	SA, CA	+	–
Lockhartia elegans	SA	+	–
Ornithocephalus cruegeri	SA	+	–
Ornithocephalus gladiatus	SA	+	+
Notylia angustifolia	SA	+	–
Notylia incurva	SA	+	–
Notylia punctata	SA	+	–
Cryptarrhena lunata	SA, CA, GA	+	–
Macradenia lutescens	SA, NA, GA	+	–
Dichaea graminoides	SA	+	–
Dichaea hookeri	SA	+	+
Dichaea hystricina	SA, CA, GA	+	+
Dichaea muricata	SA, CA, GA	+	+
Dichaea picta	SA	+	–
Dichaea rendlei	SA	+	–
Dichaea swartzii	SA, GA	–	+
Campylocentrum fasciola	SA, CA	+	–
Campylocentrum micranthum	SA, CA, GA	+	+
Campylocentrum pachyrrhizum	SA, NA	+	–
Campylocentrum pygmaeum	SA, GA	–	+